This book
belongs to

_____

Pele's
Forever
Home

Pele's Forever Home

Written by
Darylynn Ayala

Illustrated by
Jon Rothenberg

ISBN 978-1-935497-41-7

Printed in Canada
Manufactured by Friesens Corporation in
Altona, MB, Canada in August 2011
Job # 68962

Written by Darylynn Ayala

Designed by Scott Stortz

Illustrated by Jon Rothenberg

Published by:

Butler Books
P.O. Box 7311
Louisville, KY 40207
(502) 897-9393
Fax (502) 897-9797

www.butlerbooks.com

This book is dedicated to
Duke and Elli Somerville

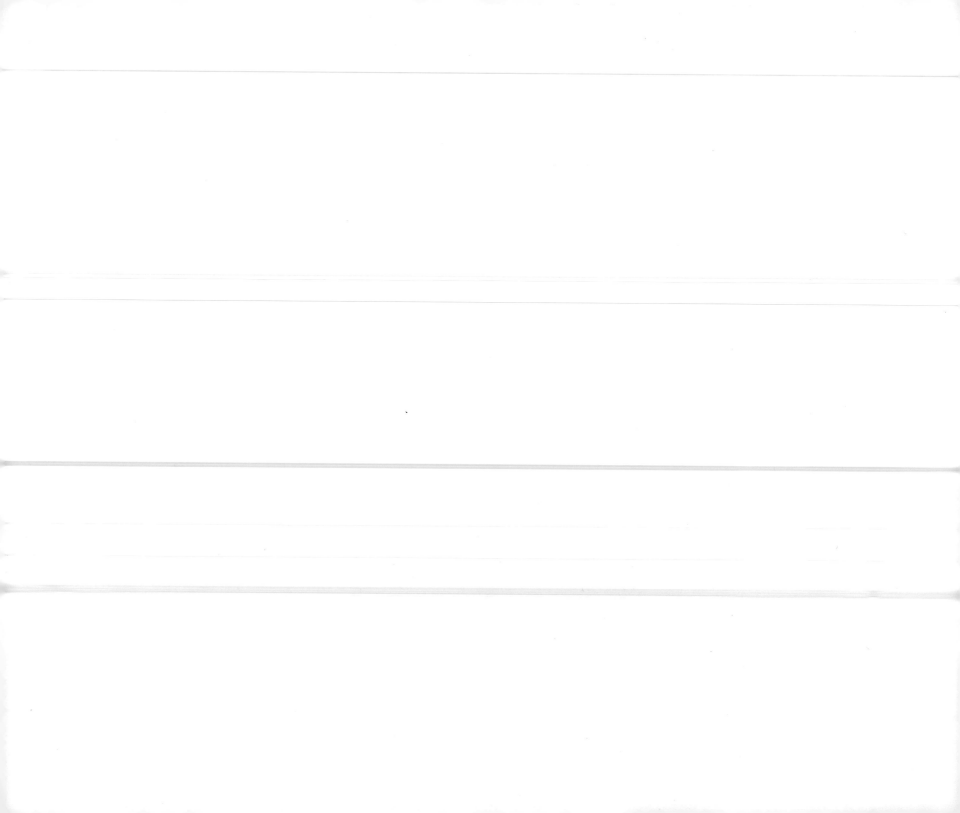

Hello, hello, my name is Pele!
I have a story to share with you today.

I am a greyhound, a special breed.
We are dogs well known for our grace and speed.

From the day I was born, I was raised to run
and told to keep running till races were won.

"Catch the rabbit," they said.
"Run, run, run!"

For me, running races was fun, fun, fun!

I was always so fast,
the best of the bunch,

and after each race, they served me lunch.

After winning each race, running fast and far, my doggie friends thought I was really a star.

At night, when we finally would rest in our spaces,
we would talk of wonderful, mysterious places

where we could run and play and roam,
a place we could call our "Forever Home."

A place we would live with a mom and a dad.
A place full of joy, where we'd never be sad.

I enjoyed being a champ and a great athlete,
but thought having a family might really be neat.

While I loved to race and win, win, win,
I dreamed of the "Forever Home" I hoped to be in.

Despite all the trophies and medals I had,
when my friends got adopted, I became very sad.

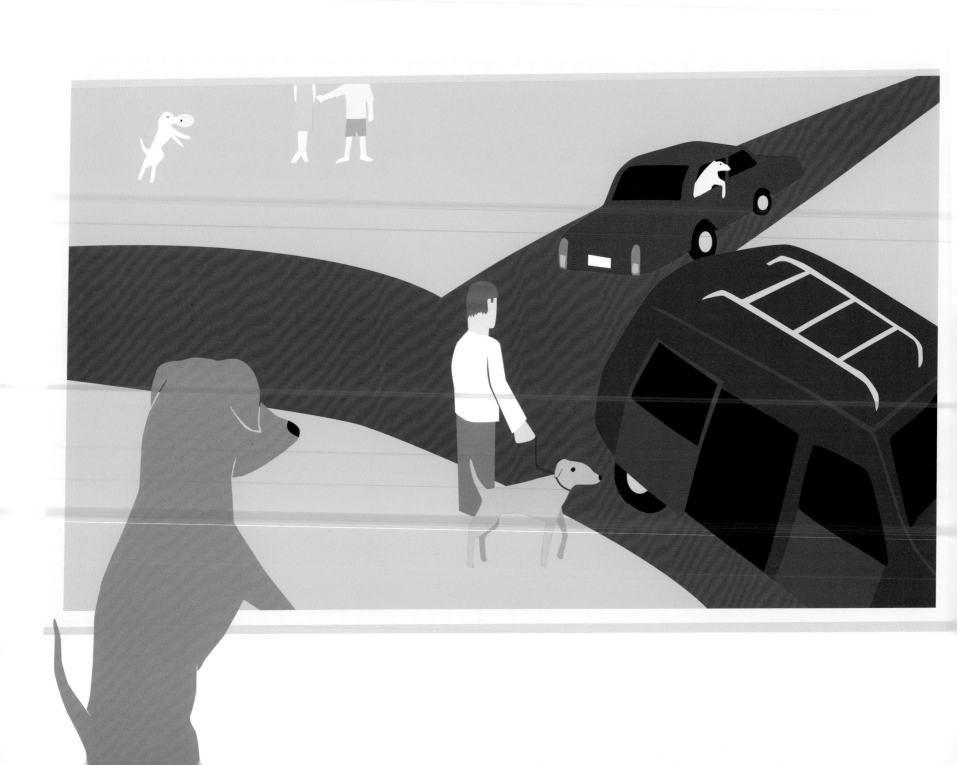

As each of them found their "Forever Home,"
I was left by myself and felt very alone.

Then one special day, quite out of the blue,
a sweet man and lady said, "We want you!"

I learned Paul and Jessica were their names,
and for hours the three of us played lots of games.

They drove me to a place very far away,
where I could be safe and be able to stay.

A place I could call my very own.
My magical place, my "Forever Home."

Many years have now passed, and I still like to run,
but taking naps in the grass is also fun.

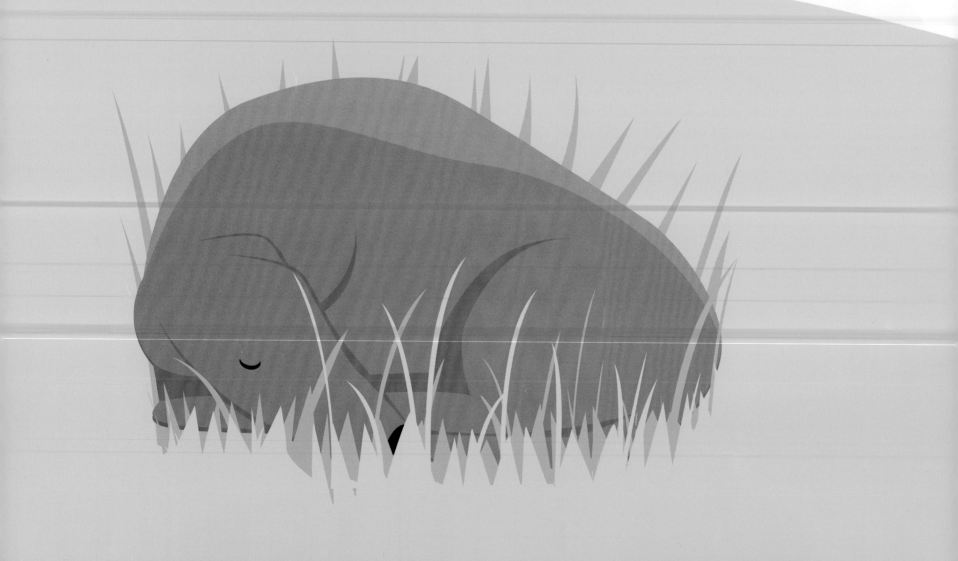

And just when I thought my life couldn't be better,
I learned that my family had gotten a letter.

A greyhound named Lucy now needed a home,
a place to run and be free to roam.

She and I live together now, peaceful and free, with our loving "Forever Home" family.

Pele

This book is a true story about a champion
greyhound named Pele, who started racing professionally at age
two and was retired at age five. Pele won 20 of the 114 races he ran
in his lifetime. When he was six years old, he was adopted by
Jessica and Paul in Boston, Massachusetts.

Pele was more than just an athlete. He was an amazing dog,
full of personality and love. He found his "Forever Home" in a family that
loved him tremendously. Sadly, Pele passed away when he was just shy
of ten years old. He is truly missed.

How to help protect Greyhounds

A percentage of proceeds from each purchased book will be donated
to non-profit greyhound protection efforts.

GREY2K USA and the GREY2K USA Education Fund work to promote the
welfare of greyhounds through advocacy, education and adoption.

Visit www.grey2kusa.org/action/adopt.html or http://www.greyhound.org/index.cfm
for more information about how you can help the greyhound community.

Help feed America's Future

A percentage of proceeds from each purchased book will also go to help feed children through the charity Blessings in a Packpack.

For more information about Blessings in a Backpack,
visit www.blessingsinabackpack.org

About the Author

Darylynn Ayala is an accomplished accessory designer, fine arts sculptor and published author who resides in New York City.

She is a strong supporter of greyhound adoptions and a passionate member of the board of directors of the Blessings in a Backpack organization.

She was inspired to do this book to bring awareness to the greyhound community, as well as Blessings in a Backpack.

About the Illustrator

Jon Rothenberg is an illustrator living in St. Louis. He received his Bachelor of Fine Arts degree from Washington University.